Copyright ©

Contents

4

What is Candida

Candidiasis, commonly referred to as "candida," is a fungal infection that can affect men and women of all ages in various parts of the body. It most commonly occurs in the mouth, ears, nose, toenails, fingernails, gastrointestinal tract and vagina. Possible symptoms comprise a true laundry list ranging from bad breath to persistent heartburn to arthritis. Due to its many and varied symptoms, candida is often ignored, undiagnosed or misdiagnosed.

If you have candida or know someone who does, the good news is that there are many candida natural treatments. The main natural treatment is a change in your diet to discourage the overgrowth of yeast.

6

Candida Risk Factors, Causes and Symptoms

Candidiasis is a fungal infection caused by yeasts that belong to the genus Candida. There are over 20 species of candida yeasts that can cause infection in humans. The most common one is Candida albicans, a single-celled fungus that's always present in the genital and intestinal tracts. Candida yeasts normally live on the skin and mucous membranes without causing infection, but overgrowth of these organisms can cause problematic symptoms to develop in the body.

Some candida risk factors include having diabetes, undergoing conventional cancer treatments and treating asthma with corticosteroid inhalants. Some women find that birth control pills seam to instigate yeast infections and even long after the initial infection is gone, once they start taking the birth control pills again, candida can take root.

According to the National Candida Center, there are are about a dozen recognized causes of intestinal dysbiosis (or dysfunction of the microbiome or inner ecology) and candida overgrowth, including:

• Poor diet

• Prescription drugs, especially antibiotics

• Alcohol consumption

• Hormone imbalance

• Tap water

8

- Digestive problems

- Stress

- Environmental molds and chemicals

- Toxic metals and food chemicals

- Immune deficiency (like having AIDS or cancer)

Do you ever experience any of these health issues?

- Exhaustion

- Cravings for sweets

- Bad breath

- White coat on tongue

- Brain fog

- Hormone imbalance

- Joint pain

- Loss of sex drive

- Chronic sinus and allergy issues

- Digestive problems (gas and bloating)

- Weak immune system

- UTI

If so, these are just some of the signs that you may have candida. Symptoms can worsen in damp or moldy environments or after consumption of food containing sugar or yeast. If left untreated, candida will weaken the immune system, allowing more serious disease to take hold.

Essential Oils for Candida

Some of the best oils to fight candida are:

- oregano oil

- myrrh oil

- lavender oil

These five all help to kill a variety of parasites and fungi, including candida, in the body. Lavender oil also inhibits the growth of candida and is effective at preventing the spread of the infection.

By mixing a couple of drops of clove oil or lavender oil with coconut oil during your cleanse, you can help to kill off the offending candida. However, since these essential oils are powerful, they should only be taken internally for 10 days or less. For oral thrush, you can use three drops of clove oil with one tablespoon of coconut oil and swish the mixture in your mouth for 20 minutes. This oil pulling is excellent for killing candida and overall detoxification of the body.

Candida Supplements

1. Probiotics (50 billion units daily): Will give your body healthy bacteria, which can help reduce the presence of yeast.

2. Oregano oil (2 drops 3 times daily for 7 days then stop): Oregano oil is naturally antibacterial and antifungal.

3. Garlic (2 caps or cloves daily): Helps fight fungal infections and boost the immune system.

4. Vitamin C (1,000 milligrams, 2–3 times daily): Boosts immune function and helps fight off infections.

5. Grapefruit seed extract (200 milligrams, 2–3 times per day): This herb has specific properties to fight candida.

In addition, you can use the following herbs to treat candida:

• astragalus

• olive leaf

A 2003 study out of Israel proved that olive leaf extracts have an antimicrobial effect against bacteria and fungi. Olive leaf extracts killed almost all bacteria tested, including dermatophytes (causing infections on the skin, hair and nails), candida albicans (an agent of oral and genital infections) and Escherichia coli cells (bacteria found in the lower intestine).

Candida Diet

The candida diet requires people to avoid foods and drinks that could increase the risk of Candida overgrowth. These include gluten, sugar, alcohol products, and certain types of dairy.

The diet focuses instead on eating lean proteins, healthful fats, nonstarchy vegetables, and probiotics. The aim of these foods is to help minimize inflammation and balance the concentrations of bacteria inside the gut.

Theoretically, people may have a lower risk of developing Candida infections if they eliminate foods that contribute to yeast growth.

How long do I need to eat like this?

In order to have success with the candida diet, it will take anywhere from a few weeks to several months. It really depends on the individual and a few key variables:

• how strictly you follow this diet

• the intake and effectiveness of probiotics and antifungals

• the severity of your candida

What to Eat

The guidelines of the Candida diet are strict and require you to completely eliminate several food groups. If you decide to embark on the diet, you should do so under the supervision of a health professional.

Compliant

- Non-starchy vegetables (artichokes, broccoli, kale, tomatoes)

- Low-sugar fruit (lemons, limes)

- Berries (in moderation, as tolerated)

- Avocado

- Olives

- Eggs

- Lean cuts of chicken or turkey

- Salmon, herring, sardines, and anchovies

- Ghee, kefir, and probiotic yogurt

- Gluten-free grains (teff, quinoa, oat bran)

- Nuts and seeds (almonds, flax, pumpkin, sunflower)

- Almond butter

- Bone broth

- Herbal tea or chicory root coffee

- Apple cider vinegar,

- Seaweed and algae

- Herbs and spices (basil, cloves, oregano, dill, garlic, ginger, cayenne)

- Stevia, monk fruit, xylitol, and erythritol

- Coconut, flax, olive, and sesame oil

- Some fermented foods (kefir, kombucha)

Non-Compliant

- Sugar (agave, aspartame, cane sugar, corn syrup, honey, molasses)

- Gluten (barley, rye, spelt, wheat)

- Packaged snack foods

- Yogurt with sugar or toppings

- Frozen meals and snacks

- Muffins, bagels, croissants, and biscuits

- Ice cream, custard, pudding, and gelatin (unless sugar-free)

- High-sugar fruits and fruit juices

- Dried fruit (dates, apricots, prunes, raisins)

- Peanuts, cashews, pistachios, and nut butters

- Processed meat (lunchmeat, hot dogs, sausage, bacon)

- Red meat and organ meat

- Tuna and swordfish

- Shellfish

- Full-fat milk, cheese, cream, and other dairy products

- Bottled salad dressings, dips, and condiments

- Canola oil, sunflower oil, soybean oil, margarine, or "butter" sprays

- Fruit juice, energy drinks, and soft drinks

- Caffeinated coffee, tea, or sodas

- Alcohol

Fruits and vegetables: Fresh, frozen, canned, and dried fruits that are high in sugar are excluded on the Candida diet. Juices made from these fruits, or those that are sweetened, should also be avoided. Low-sugar fruits like limes and lemons are OK, as are small portions of berries.

For vegetables, stick to non-starchy options like broccoli, kale, and tomatoes. Produce that is likely to be exposed to mold, such as mushrooms, should be avoided.

Dairy: Full-fat dairy is limited on the Candida diet with the exception of probiotic yogurt, ghee, and real butter (in moderation). All sugary milk or yogurt products, such as ice cream or frozen yogurt, are banned. Moldy blue cheeses, processed cheese, cream cheese, and cheese dipping snacks are also not allowed.

Grains: Many Candida diets recommended the avoidance of wheat and gluten, but there is insufficient evidence that this can help. Likewise, some Candida diets advise the restriction of food made with yeast, though the evidence for this is also lacking.

If you decide to cut gluten from your diet, it is generally best to do so if you experience gluten intolerance or gluten sensitivity rather than as a means to control Candida.

Protein: Lean protein, such as eggs and skinless poultry, are allowed on the Candida diet, as are bone broth and certain fatty fish. Low-mold nuts and seeds are also approved.

The Candida diet also excludes red, organ, and processed meats. Shellfish and large fish (like tuna and swordfish) are also excluded as they are more likely to have been exposed to heavy metals like mercury.

Beverages: Alcohol is banned on the Candida diet. Fermented drinks like cider and root beer are also to be avoided. The same applies to sodas or energy drinks, whether they are sugar-free or not. Fruit juices, smoothies, milkshakes, milk-based coffee drinks, and other sweetened beverages (like hot chocolate) are also on the banned list.

Caffeinated coffee and tea are allowed in small amounts if they don't contain sugar, dairy, or non-dairy creamer. Herbal teas and chicory root coffee are acceptable beverages, as long as they are caffeine- and sugar-free.

Desserts: The primary foods to avoid on the Candida diet are those containing sugar, so very few dessert options are compliant.

Avoid any food made with refined sugar, including table sugar, brown sugar, honey, maple syrup, corn syrup, maple sugar, molasses, date sugar, raw sugar, rice syrup, or sorghum. This not only includes cakes and cookies but many breads.

Check nutrition labels for other names for sugar, such as sucrose, fructose, maltose, lactose, glucose, dextrose, galactose, barley malt, dextrin, turbinado, monosaccharide, and polysaccharide.

The Candida diet does allow for sugar substitutes such as stevia, monk fruit, xylitol, and erythritol.

Herbs and spices like cinnamon and ginger can be used to add flavor and a certain sweetness.

Recommended Timing

There's no set schedule for meals on the Candida diet, so you can adapt it to your needs. Because the diet is so restrictive, you should have plenty of small snacks on hand to nibble throughout the day if ever you feel weak or lightheaded.

Some people on the Candida diet prefer to eat frequent, smaller meals rather than three large ones. It may be the ideal choice for people with diabetes in that it helps stabilize blood sugar levels and prevent hypoglycemia. It can also prevent symptoms like diabetic gastroparesis, which can make you feel full after only eating a few bites.

Cooking Tips

When preparing for the Candida diet, take the time to find substitutes for the foods you enjoy. Doing so can help you feel less deprived and keep you on the diet longer.

There are several easy swaps to consider:

• You can make a carb-free meal by pairing lean cuts of poultry with a side of cauliflower "rice" or by using lettuce to wrap a turkey burger instead of a bun.

• If you're looking for ways to sweeten a meal naturally without sugar, try monk fruit. The naturally sweet melon works for just about any dish, including teas, oatmeal, and sauces.

• In place of mayonnaise-based dressings, make a tasty yogurt dressing with plain non-fat yogurt, lemon juice, poppy seeds, dried mustard, and a touch of stevia.

Modifications

There are times when the Candida diet may not be safe without significant modifications, it at all. If you are being treated for diabetes, for example, it may not be safe to reduce your sugar intake as strictly as the diet demands. Doing so can lead to a potentially serious hypoglycemic event.

While yeast infections are common during pregnancy, embarking on any restricted diet during pregnancy is potentially harmful to you and your baby and should be avoided. If anything, you will need to increase your nutritional intake during pregnancy to meet your body's increased energy needs and promote healthy fetal development.

On the other hand, if you have celiac disease, are lactose intolerant, or follow a vegan or vegetarian diet, you may already be adhering to many of the diet recommendations. Just be sure that the additional changes don't leave you nutritionally deprived and lacking the protein and carbohydrates need to function normally.

Precautions: Possible Candida Die-Off Symptoms

Rapidly killing off candida in your body creates a metabolic reaction that releases over 70 different toxins into your body. Sounds pretty intense, right? Well before you get scared off, what you may or may not have to deal with as a result of candida die-off is definitely preferable to what you have to deal with if you let the candida continue to internally flourish.

Symptoms that show the candida cleanse and the candida diet are working include:

• Impaired brain function

• Headache

• Fatigue

• Dizziness

• Intestinal distress, including bloating, gas, constipation and nausea

• Sweating and fever

• Sinus infection

• Skin breakouts (not limited to face)

- Typical flu-like symptoms

These symptoms usually clear up in seven to 10 days. The candida is leaving your body, and within just a few weeks, you will notice an increase in energy and focus, as well as relief from other symptoms you have experienced. So when you start to experience candida die-off symptoms, it's time to celebrate because you are on your way to better health!

After your symptoms have subsided and you have completed the cleanse and the candida diet, you should continue eating a diet that's high in protein and high-fiber vegetables, and limit grains, fruits, sugar and high-starch vegetables like white potatoes. Continue to consume fermented vegetables and kefir to help your body stay in balance and keep the candida at bay.

If you have chronic or unusually persistent candida infections, you should consult your health care provider. This could be a sign of an underlying illness, such as diabetes or immune system dysfunction, which makes for an environment more conducive to the growth of candida.

Recipes

You definitely want to eat a mix of raw, fermented and cooked vegetables while on the candida diet. When it comes to recipes, you of course want ones that leave out all of the candida-promoting foods above while including as many of the candida killers as possible.

CANDIDA DIET RECIPES

In this part are recipes to keep your candida at bay.

Green Smoothie

Preparation time

5 minutes

INGREDIENTS

- 16 oz. homemade nondairy milk

- 1 c. fresh spinach

- 1/2 avocado

- 5 frozen strawberries

- 1 Tbsp. chia seeds

- 1/4 tsp. cinnamon

- liquid stevia to taste

Optional: DIY Protein Powder

INSTRUCTIONS

1. Throw everything into your Black and Decker Personal Blender until smooth.

2. Adjust flavor with liquid stevia.

Avocado Baked Eggs with Vegetable Hash

Preparation time

30 minutes

Ingredients

- 1/4 cup diced tomato

- 1/4 cup diced zucchini

- 1/4 cup diced yellow pepper

- 1/4 cup diced onion

- 2 Tbsp. olive oil, divided

- 1 avocado, halved and seeded

- 2 eggs, medium or large

- Salt and pepper to taste

- Fresh parsley, finely minced (optional)

Instructions

1. Preheat oven to 425 degrees F (220 degrees C)

2. In the bottom of a small oven proof casserole dish, add the diced vegetables, stir to mix, then spread out evenly. Sprinkle vegetable mixture with salt and pepper and drizzle with one tablespoon of olive oil.

3. Create two wells in the mixture and place an avocado half in each. Crack an egg into each avocado half, sprinkle with salt and pepper and drizzle with remaining tablespoon of olive oil.

4. Bake for 15 to 20 minutes or until eggs whites are set and yolks are starting to thicken.

5. Sprinkle with minced parsley (optional) and serve.

Asian Chicken and Cabbage Salad

Preparation time

30 minutes

Ingredients

- Dressing

- 2 Tbsp. olive oil

- 2 Tbsp. sesame oil

- 2 Tbsp. apple cider vinegar

- 2 Tbsp. coconut aminos

- 1/4 tsp. garlic powder

- 1/4 tsp. onion powder

- 1/4 tsp. powdered ginger

- 1/4 tsp. powdered stevia

- Salt and pepper to taste

Salad

- 1 large shallot

- Light oil such as olive or avocado

- 2 cups cooked shredded chicken

- 4 cups shredded green cabbage

- 1 cup shredded purple cabbage

- 1 cup broccoli florets

- 1/4 cup sliced green onions

- 1/4 cup cilantro leaves

- 1 Tbsp. sesame seeds

Instructions

1. To make the dressing, add olive oil, sesame oil, apple cider vinegar, coconut aminos, garlic powder, onion powder, powdered ginger, powdered stevia, salt and pepper to taste into a small bowl. Whisk to combine, set dressing aside.

2. To prepare fried shallots, slice shallot into thin rings.

3. Place rings into a pan with an inch of light oil such as olive or avocado.

4. Heat oil over high heat and wait for shallot rings to begin bubble.

5. Lower heat to medium and wait for bubbles to subside and rings to turn golden brown, about 8 to 10 minutes.

6. Transfer fried shallots to a plate lined with paper towel and cool completely, set aside.

7. To make the salad, add cooked shredded chicken, shredded green cabbage, shredded purple cabbage, broccoli florets, sliced green onions, sliced almonds, cilantro leaves and sesame seeds in a large bowl, toss lightly.

8. Pour dressing over salad, toss lightly to combine.

9. Garnish salad with fried shallots, serve immediately.

Curried Chicken Bowl

Prep Time

20 mins

Ingredients

Dressing

- 2 tablespoons olive oil

- 2 tablespoons canned coconut milk

- 1 tablespoon fresh lemon juice

- 1/2 teaspoon minced garlic

- 1/2 teaspoon powdered turmeric

- 1/2 teaspoon powdered ginger

- 1/4 teaspoon powdered stevia

- Salt and pepper to taste

Salad

- 1 1/2 cups cooked chicken, white or dark meat, shredded or cubed

- 1/4 cup diced celery

- 1/4 cup diced Granny Smith apple

- 2 tablespoons finely chopped red onion

- 2 tablespoons slivered almonds

- 1 cup fresh spinach leaves

- 1 cup cooked quinoa

- Fresh cilantro for garnish

Instructions

1. To make dressing, in a small bowl add olive oil, canned coconut milk, fresh lemon juice, minced garlic, powdered turmeric, powdered ginger, powdered stevia, salt and pepper.

2. Whisk to combine, set dressing aside.

3. To make salad, in a medium bowl add cooked, shredded chicken, diced celery, diced Granny Smith apple, finely chopped red onion and slivered almonds.

4. Mix well.

5. Pour dressing over the salad, toss to combine.

4)

6. To assemble, fill a bowl with spinach leaves, cooked quinoa and curried chicken salad.

7. Garnish with cilantro. Enjoy!

Mediterranean Zucchini Dip

Courgettes

Preparation time

1 hour 20 minutes

Ingredients

- 1 Tbsp. oil olive or coconut

- 2 medium zucchini (about 1 pound) grated

- 1/4 cup onions diced

- 1/2 tsp. salt

- 1 small garlic clove minced

- Pepper

- 1/4 tsp. ground coriander

- 1/2 tsp. lemon zest

- 1 Tbsp. lemon juice

- 1 Tbsp. fresh minced herbs such as basil, mint or parsley

- 1/4 cup plain Greek style yogurt

Instructions

1. Heat oil in a large skillet over medium heat.

2. Add grated zucchini, diced onions and salt. Cover and simmer for 10 minutes, stirring

halfway. Uncover skillet, add minced garlic and pepper to taste, sauté for 30 seconds.

3. Remove skillet from heat, cool vegetables to room temperature, about 1 hour.

4. In the bowl of a food processor, add cooled cooked vegetables, ground coriander, lemon zest and juice, fresh minced herbs and yogurt.

5. Process until mixture is smooth.

6. Serve dip with crackers or a platter of assorted roasted vegetables.

Zucchini Noodle Salad with Grilled Steak

Preparation time

30 minutes

Ingredients

- 1 medium steak, grilled and thinly sliced

- 1 to 2 medium zucchinis cut into "noodles" with a spiral slicer, julienne peeler or mandolin

- 2 scallions, thinly sliced diagonally

- ¼ cup finely minced herbs, like mint, cilantro and parsley

- 1 Tbsp. olive oil

- 1 tsp. coconut aminos

• Salt and pepper

Instructions

1. In a large bowl, combine zucchini noodles, sliced scallions and minced herb mixture.

2. Reserve a few minced herbs for the garnish.

3. Cover salad and chill until ready to serve.

4. Make dressing by whisking together olive oil, coconut aminos, salt and pepper to taste in a small bowl, or by placing all ingredients in a small jar with a lid and shaking well.

5. Pour dressing over salad just before serving and toss to combine.

6. Top salad with strips of thinly sliced grilled steak, sprinkle with herbs, serve immediately.

Chicken Zucchini Burgers

Preparation time

30 minutes

Ingredients

- 1 lb. chicken breasts

- 1 large zucchini (diced)

- 1 garlic clove (crushed)

- 2 spring onions (finely chopped)

- 3 Tbsp. ground almonds

- 1 tsp. smoked paprika

- 2 tsp. coconut aminos

- Large handful fresh parsley

- Salt and pepper to taste

- 1 Tbsp. coconut oil

Instructions

1. Place all of the ingredients apart from the oil into a food processor.

2. Process until smooth and holding together.

3. Using oiled hands (to avoid sticking) form into 4 patties.

4. Heat the oil in a large non stick skillet over a medium heat.

5. Cook the patties, 2 at a time in the pan, for around 3-4 minutes on each side until golden brown and cooked through.

Coconut Ginger Clouds

Preparation time

30 minutes

Ingredients

1. 3 egg whites

2. 2 packets or 1 tsp. powdered Stevia

3. 1 Tbsp. alcohol free vanilla

4. 1 tsp. fresh ginger, peeled and finely grated with a microplane

5. 1 cup unsweetened shredded coconut

6. 1 cup unsweetened coconut flakes

Instructions

1. Preheat oven to 350 degrees F (177 degrees C).

2. In a large bowl, whisk egg whites until light and foamy. Add stevia, alcohol free vanilla and ginger, whisk to combine. Fold in shredded coconut and coconut flakes until just combined.

3. Line a baking sheet with parchment paper. Drop tablespoon size mounds of coconut mixture onto baking sheet. Bake for 10 to 12 minutes or until cookies just begin to brown. Cool on baking sheet for 10 minutes before removing.

Shamrock Shake

Preparation time

10 minutes

INGREDIENTS

- 1 large cucumber or two small ones

- 1/2 avocado or 1 small avocado

- 1 dash coconut milk you can make your own!

- 3/4 cup baby spinach

- 1 handful peppermint leaves or 4 drops peppermint essential oil or peppermint extract, to taste

- 1 handful ice optional

INSTRUCTIONS

1. Peel and cut the cucumber(s) into small chunks, and place into a blender with the rest of the ingredients.

2. Blend until smooth

3. Enjoy!

Cinnamon cookies

Preparation time

20 minutes

Ingredients

1. 3 Tablespoons Coconut Oil, softened

2. 1 1/2 Tablespoons Natural Unsweetened Almond, Cashew or Sunflower Seed Butter

3. 3 Tablespoons Xylitol

4. 1 Large Egg if your eggs are small, please use 2 eggs

5. 1/4 teaspoon Baking Soda

6. 1/2 teaspoon Baking Powder

7. 1/4 teaspoon Sea or Pink Salt

8. 1 teaspoon Pure Vanilla Extract

9. 1 teaspoon Cinnamon

10. 3 Tablespoons Coconut Flour or 5-7 Tablespoons whole grain flour, like Whole Spelt Flour

Instructions

1. Pre-heat oven to 350 degrees.

2. In a small bowl, mix together the coconut oil, nut butter and xylitol together until combined.

3. Add the egg and mix well.

4. Add the baking soda, baking powder, salt and vanilla.

5. Add the cinnamon and flour and mix until combined.

6. Scoop out the dough with a small cookie scoop and roll into smooth spheres.

7. Place on a parchment lined baking sheet.

8. Bake for 7-9 minutes.

9. Allow to cool on the pan for AT LEAST 3 minutes. Enjoy!

Keto Gut-Healing Paleo Pancakes

Preparation time

10 minutes

Ingredients:

- 2 large eggs

- 1.5 tbsp ground flaxseeds

- 1 scoop Vital Proteins Vanilla Collagen (or sub Vital Proteins regular collagen plus 2 tbsp vanilla, or sub protein powder of choice)

- dash of cinnamon

- dash of pink salt

- some coconut oil for your skillet

Toppings: any you want! Nut butter, berries, nuts, shredded coconut, cacao nibs, etc.

Instructions:

1. Mix the eggs, flax, collagen, cinnamon, and salt together in a bowl and let sit for 5 minutes

to thicken a bit. (If you want to be fancy, I recommend mixing some toppings into the batter! Cacao nibs, shredded coconut, even berries...)

2. Heat up the coconut oil in your skillet until melted and covering the skillet. Pour the batter into the skillet in circles to make the pancakes however large you want.

3. Let the pancakes cook until the edges are cooked and the bottom is slightly browned. Flip and repeat until the other side is cooked. Continue until you've used all the batter.

4. Add your toppings and enjoy!

Oat Bran-Buckwheat Carrot Cake Porridge

Preparation time

20 minutes

INGREDIENTS

- 40g oat bran

- 40g roasted buckwheat porridge flakes

- 400g water

- 50g soy milk *non*

- 1 tsp. (not heaped) cinnamon

- ½ tsp. (not heaped) ginger powder

58

- ¼ tsp. gingerbread spice or cardamom (optional)

- Himalayan salt to taste

- Sweetener of choice to taste (brich xylitol or stevia)

- 50g of finely grated carrot

INSTRUCTIONS

1. Measure your oat bran and buckwheat flakes.

2. Bring water to boil.

3. Reduce the heat and pour in oat bran whisking vigorously. Keep on whisking and simmering for 6 minutes.

4. Add soy milk and bring to boil again.

5. Mix in buckwheat flakes and simmer for 1 minute whisking at the same time.

6. Turn off the heat, cover with lid and let sit for 2 minutes.

7. Add salt, taste and adjust until it is to your satisfaction. Repeat the same with sweetener.

8. Throw in cinnamon, ginger powder and gingerbread spice and mix well. Taste and adjust if necessary.

9. Finally mix in finely grated carrots.

Mindful Veggie Bowl

Preparation time

Ingredients

INGREDIENTS FOR VEGGIE BOWL

- 4 cups fresh vegetables, such as cauliflower, broccoli, celery, zucchini *Courgette*

- 1 clove garlic, thinly sliced

- 1 Tbsp. oil, such as olive or coconut

- 1 tsp. Seasoning Mix (see below)

- 1 leaf Swiss *spinach* chard, sliced into ribbons

- 2 Tbsp. sliced almonds

- Olive or coconut oil

- Coconut aminos or lemon juice

- Red pepper flakes to taste

INGREDIENTS FOR SEASONING MIX

- 1 tsp. salt

- ½ tsp. turmeric

- ¼ tsp. cayenne

- 1/8 tsp. curry powder

Instructions

DIRECTIONS FOR VEGGIE BOWL

1. Preheat oven to 400 degrees F (205 degrees C).

2. Place vegetables directly on a rimmed baking sheet, drizzle with oil and sprinkle with Seasoning Mix. Roast 10 to 15 minutes, until vegetables begin to brown.

3. In a large bowl, add roasted vegetables, Swiss chard ribbons and sliced almonds, toss to combine.

4. Serve in deep bowls, drizzle with a bit of oil, a dash of coconut aminos or lemon juice and a pinch of red pepper flakes.

DIRECTIONS FOR SEASONING MIX

1. Combine all ingredients in a jar.

2. Put lid on jar and shake well until mixed.

Baba Ganoush

Preparation time

20 minutes

Ingredients:

- 1 eggplant

- 1/4 cup tahini

- Juice of 1 lemon

- 1/2 tsp sea salt or pink Himalayan salt

Optional: extra virgin olive oil for topping

Instructions:

1. Turn the heat on your stovetop on medium-high.

2. Place the whole eggplant on top of the heat.

3. Let it grill up so that it softens up, turning the eggplant after each side is done so that the whole thing grills.

4. Leave each side on the flames for about 5-7 minutes, turn it, and continue doing so until it's grilled all over. The skin will look "cracked" and will be soft enough so that you can peel it off.

5. Peel about 80% of the eggplant, and leave the rest of the skin on (just a little).

6. Place it in the food processor.

7. Add the tahini, lemon juice, and salt.

8. Puree everything in the food processor until the mixture is smooth. I like to leave a few chunks in mine for a little bit of texture, but it should be pretty smooth.

9. Add more tahini, salt, or lemon to taste.

10. Top with olive oil for extra flavor and longevity! Enjoy!

Nachos With Rutabaga Chips

Preparation time

40 minutes

Ingredients

INGREDIENTS FOR RUTABAGA CHIPS

- 3 large rutabaga, peeled and sliced

- 3 Tbsp. oil, such as olive or coconut (melted)

- 1 tsp. salt

INGREDIENTS FOR SEASONED NACHO MEAT

- ½ Tbsp. oil, such as olive or coconut

- 1 pound ground meat, such as beef, bison or turkey

- 1 Tbsp. chili powder

- 2 tsps. onion powder

- 1 tsp. ground cumin

- 1 tsp. garlic powder

- 1 tsp. paprika

- 1 tsp. dried oregano

- 1 tsp. salt

- 1 cup water

INGREDIENTS FOR NACHOS

- Rutabaga chips (see above)

- Seasoned nacho meat (see above)

- Red pepper, seeded and diced

- Red onion, thinly sliced

- Green onion, thinly sliced

- Fresh cilantro, minced

- Guacamole

- Plain yogurt

Instructions

INSTRUCTIONS FOR RUTABAGA CHIPS

1. Preheat oven to 400 degrees F (205 degrees C).

2. Peel rutabagas, then with a sharp knife or mandoline, slice thinly.

3. In a large mixing bowl, add rutabaga slices and oil, toss to coat evenly.

4. Spread slices in a single layer on a lightly oiled baking sheet, sprinkle with salt.

5. Bake 25 to 30 minutes, flipping halfway to ensure even browning.

6. Repeat with remaining rutabaga slices.

7. Transfer rutabaga chips to paper toweling to absorb excess oil.

8. Chips will continue to crisp as they cool.

INSTRUCTIONS FOR SEASONED NACHO MEAT

1. In a large skillet, heat oil over medium heat.

2. Add ground meat and cook until browned, about 5 minutes, stirring occasionally to break up meat.

3. Add chili powder, onion powder, ground cumin, garlic powder, paprika, dried oregano and salt, stir to combine.

4. Add water, bring to a simmer and cook, uncovered, until liquid has evaporated, 15 to 20 minutes.

5. Remove meat from heat.

FINISHING THE NACHOS

1. Place a layer of rutabaga chips on a plate.

2. Spoon on seasoned meat mixture, top with guacamole and plain yogurt, then garnish with diced red pepper, sliced red and green onion and fresh minced cilantro.

Marinated Kale Salad Recipe

Preparation time

15 minutes

Ingredients

- 1 large bunch of organic Lacinato kale about 4 cups

- Zest and juice of one lemon

- 1/3 cup sun-dried tomatoes in oil
- 2 Tablespoons olive oil
- 1 Tablespoon apple cider vinegar
- 1/2 teaspoon sea salt
- 1/4 cup pumpkin or sunflower seeds
- 1/2 avocado diced

Instructions

1. Wash and dry kale leaves. Remove the stems by holding the end of the stem with one hand and pulling the leaf off towards the top end with the other hand. Set the stems aside for use at another time. Chop kale leaves into bite-size pieces and place in large bowl. Zest lemon over leaves and pour in the sun-dried tomatoes

(allowing a little oil from the sun-dried tomato jar to go in as well).

2. In a separate, smaller bowl, whisk together olive oil, lemon juice, apple cider vinegar, and sea salt. Pour mixture over kale.* Using your hands, massage the mixture into the leaves for about 2-3 minutes. You will see and feel the kale getting softer in your hands.

3. Finally, add the pumpkin or sunflower seeds and diced avocado on top.

4. Taste for seasoning.

Buckwheat And Brussels Sprout Salad

Preparation time

40 minutes

Ingredients

- 2 cups water

- 1 cup whole buckwheat groats

- Pinch of salt

- 2 Tbsp. oil, such as extra virgin olive or coconut

- ¼ cup shallots, thinly sliced

- ¼ cup celery, thinly sliced

- 1 clove garlic, minced

- 8 Brussels sprouts, cut in half lengthwise

- 1 Tbsp. fresh thyme leaves (or 1 teaspoon dried thyme)

- 1 cup vegetable broth or water

- Salt and pepper to taste

- 2 to 3 leaves Swiss chard, cut across into ribbons

- Fresh herbs, such as thyme or parsley, minced

- Crushed, toasted nuts, such as hazelnuts, pecans or walnuts

Instructions

1. In a medium saucepan, bring water and salt to a boil.

2. Add whole buckwheat groats, cover and simmer for 15 to 20 minutes.

3. Remove from heat, let rest for 5 minutes, fluff with a fork.

4. While buckwheat groats are simmering, heat oil in a large skillet over medium heat.

5. Add shallots, celery, garlic, Brussels sprouts and saute until vegetables begin to soften and brown (about 5 minutes).

6. Next, add fresh or dried thyme leaves, broth or water, salt and pepper to taste and simmer covered over medium low heat for about 10 minutes.

76

7. Then add the Swiss chard, stirring to wilt for about 1 to 2 minutes.

8. Lastly, add cooked buckwheat groats to the skillet, and stir to combine.

9. To serve, you can garnish with fresh minced herbs and crushed, toasted nuts. For a salad, cool it to room temperature and toss with 2 to 3 tablespoons of extra virgin olive oil and 1 tablespoon of lemon juice.

Sesame Salmon Burgers

Preparation time

12 minutes

Ingredients

- 1 pound salmon, skin removed

- 1 tablespoon toasted sesame oil

- 1 tablespoon ume plum vinegar

- 1 clove garlic, pressed

- 1 teaspoon peeled and minced fresh ginger

- ¼ cup chopped scallions, white and green parts

- ¼ cup toasted raw sesame seeds

- 2 large eggs

- 1 tablespoon coconut flour

- coconut oil, for frying

Instructions

1. Rinse salmon, pat dry and cut into ¼-inch cubes

2. In a large bowl, combine salmon, oil, ume, garlic, ginger, scallions, sesame seeds, and eggs

3. Stir coconut flour into mixture

4. Use a ¼ cup measuring cup to form mixture into patties

5. Heat coconut oil in a 9 inch skillet over medium-high heat

6. Cook patties for 4 to 6 minutes per side, until golden brown

7. Transfer patties to a paper towel-lined plate and serve hot.

Kimchi Meatballs

Preparation time

30 minutes

Ingredients

- Meatballs

- 1 Tbsp. olive oil

- 1 lb. ground turkey/chicken

- 2 scallions, finely minced

- 1 clove garlic, finely minced

- 1 Tbsp. fresh cilantro, finely minced *parsley*

- 1 egg yolk, lightly beaten

- 1 tsp. sesame oil

- 1 tsp. ginger, freshly grated

- 1/2 tsp. salt

- 1/2 tsp. pepper

- 3 Tbsp. kimchi, minced

- Sauce & Garnish

- 2 Tbsp. coconut aminos

- 2 Tbsp. sesame oil

- 0.5 cucumbers, cut into 24 slices

- 4 radishes, cut into 24 slices

- 1 Tbsp. sesame seeds

- 2 Tbsp. cilantro, finely minced

Instructions

1. Preheat oven to 400 degrees F (205 degrees C).

2. Brush a rimmed baking sheet with a tablespoon of oil, set aside.

3. In large bowl, mix together ground turkey, finely minced scallions, garlic and fresh cilantro, lightly beaten egg yolk, sesame oil, fresh grated or powdered ginger, salt, pepper and minced kimchi.

4. With wet hands, form meat mixture into 24 meatballs.

5. Place meatballs on oiled baking sheet, about an inch apart and bake 20 minutes. Remove meatballs from oven, cool slightly.

6. In a small bowl, whisk together coconut aminos and sesame oil, set aside.

7. To assemble appetizer, place a radish slice on top of a cucumber slice, then top with a meatball, repeat to make 24 appetizers.

8. Drizzle coconut amino/sesame oil mixture over the meatballs. Garnish appetizers with sesame seeds and finely minced cilantro.

Green Chili Chicken Stew

Preparation time

40 minutes

Ingredients

- 2 Tbsp. oil, such as olive or coconut

- ½ cup zucchini, cut lengthwise, then into 1/2 inch slices

- ½ cup yellow squash, cut lengthwise, then into 1/2 inch slices

- ½ cup coarsely chopped onion

- 2 celery stalks, thinly sliced

- 2 garlic cloves, minced

- 4 cups chicken broth

- 8 oz. cooked, shredded chicken

- ½ cup chopped green chilies (see note above)

- 1 tsp. dried oregano

- ½ tsp. salt

- ¼ tsp. pepper

- 2 Tbsp. lime juice

- Avocado slices (optional)

- Fresh cilantro (optional)

- Lime wedges (optional)

Instructions

1. In a Dutch oven, heat oil over medium heat. Add the zucchini, yellow squash, onion, celery, and garlic and cook, stirring occasionally, until beginning to soften, about 5 minutes.

2. Add chicken broth and bring to a boil. Reduce heat and add shredded chicken, green chilies, dried oregano, salt and pepper.

3. Simmer stew covered over medium low heat for 15 to 20 minutes. Stir in lime juice just

before serving. Garnish bowls of stew with sliced avocado, fresh cilantro and lime wedges.

4. Stews and soups are excellent options for cold winter nights on the Candida diet. Our Ultimate Candida Diet program is packed full of gluten-free, sugar-free recipes like this. It contains more than 100 recipes in total, and they're all perfect for the Candida diet. Find out more here.

Course Breakfast

Preparation time

30 minutes.

Ingredients

- 2 tablespoons coconut flour

- 3/4 cup blanched almond flour

- 4 tablespoons arrowroot powder

- 1 teaspoon baking soda

- 1 teaspoon sea salt

- 6 organic or pastured eggs room temperature

- 1 1/2 tablespoons vanilla extract

- 2 tablespoons coconut oil barely melted

- 1 to 2 cups organic strawberries frozen, then thawed and mashed

Instructions

1. Stir together coconut flour, almond flour, arrowroot powder, and sea salt in a medium-sized bowl. Set aside.

2. Mix together eggs, vanilla extract, and melted coconut oil in blender on high until mixture is frothy.

3. Pour dry mix into the blender, and mix well.

4. Let batter sit for about 2 to 3 minutes so the coconut flour will soak up more of the liquid.

5. Add baking soda to blender and give it a quick whirl.

6. Pour about 1/4 cup of batter onto a hot, lightly greased griddle.

7. When the pancake batter forms bubbles, and the batter looks like it's starting to dry a bit

88

(about 1 to 2 minutes), flip the pancake over and cook on the other side.

8. Once the second side is lightly browned, remove from heat onto a plate covered with a tea towel.

9. Repeat with the rest of the batter.

10. Serve pancakes topped with mashed strawberries. Enjoy!

Cabbage Masala

Preparation time

35 minutes

Ingredients

- ½ head of cabbage

- 1 large Onion

- 2 large tomatoes

- ¾ cup okra

- 5 garlic cloves

- 3 Tbsp. coconut oil

- 1 tsp. mustard seeds

- 1 tsp. cumin powder

- 1 tsp. garam masala

- ¼ tsp. turmeric

- 1 tsp. sea salt

Instructions

1. Finely slice the cabbage, onion, tomatoes, okra and garlic cloves, then set them aside.

2. Heat some oil in a pan and add the mustard seeds. Once they pop, add the sliced garlic cloves and cook until slightly soft.

3. Next, add the onion and cook until soft. Lastly, add the turmeric powder, garam masala, and cumin powder, and cook for another 2-3 minutes.

4. Now add the tomatoes to the pan. Cover and cook for 5 minutes.

5. Lastly, add the cabbage, okra, and salt. Cook for a further 15 minutes.

Keto Cinnamon Waffles with Coconut Glaze

Preparation time

34 minutes

Tools

- Small saucepan

- Medium mixing bowl

- Small mixing bowl

- Waffle maker

Ingredients

92

For the Coconut Cream Topping:

- 1/2 cup coconut cream

- 1 T coconut butter

- 1/2 t vanilla extract

- 1/8 t cinnamon

- 1/8 t monk fruit powder

For the Waffles:

- 5 large eggs

- 1/3 cup unsweetened almond milk

- 1/2 t vanilla extract

- 1½ cups blanched almond flour

- 1/8 t monk fruit powder

- 2 t cinnamon

- 1/2 t baking powder

- 1/8 t sea salt

- 1 T melted ghee for greasing

Instructions

1. Heat ingredients for the coconut cream topping over medium-low heat in a small saucepan until smooth and steaming, about 5 minutes.

2. Turn the heat off and pour into a small serving dish.

3. Whisk together the eggs, almond milk, and vanilla extract in a medium mixing bowl until thoroughly combined.

4. In a separate small mixing bowl, stir together the almond flour, monk fruit powder, cinnamon, baking powder, and sea salt.

5. Gradually whisk the dry ingredients into the wet to form a smooth batter.

6. Heat the waffle maker on medium-high setting and grease with 1 teaspoon of ghee.

7. Once heated, pour ½ cup of batter on the center of waffle maker and close the lid.

8. Cook about 5 to 6 minutes.

9. Use a rubber spatula to gently transfer each waffle to a plate and repeat with the remaining batter.

10. Grease with more ghee as needed.

11. Serve waffles hot, drizzled with coconut glaze.

Turkey and Egg Breakfast Skillet

Preparation time

25 minutes

Ingredients

- 1 T extra virgin olive oil

- ½ onion, finely chopped

- ½ lb ground turkey

- 1 cup organic tomato sauce (no sugar added)

- 2 eggs

- Salt and pepper, to taste

Instructions

1. Heat the olive oil in the skillet over medium heat.

2. Add the chopped onion and sauté until soft and translucent.

3. Add the ground turkey and cook until fully browned.

4. Add in the tomato sauce and continue to cook for 2-3 minutes.

5. Season with salt and pepper.

6. Make 2 small wells in the turkey mixture and crack the eggs into each.

7. Cover the skillet and cook for 5 minutes or until the egg whites are opaque.

Broccoli Muffins

Preparation time

35 minutes

Tools

- Muffin tin

- Mixing bowl

Ingredients

- 2 t ghee, softened + extra for greasing

- 1 cup broccoli florets, finely chopped

- 2 cups almond flour

- 2 large pasture-raised eggs

- 1 cup unsweetened almond milk

- 2 T nutritional yeast

- 1 t baking powder

- 1/2 t sea salt

Instructions

1. Preheat the oven to 350°F and grease a large muffin tin with ghee.

2. Stir together all the ingredients in a large mixing bowl until well combined.

3. Spoon the mixture into the muffin tins. Bake for 30 minutes until a toothpick inserted in the center comes out clean.

Pages.
Not numbered. Not UK foods
Yeast = p98 !
Monk Fruit Powder p92
Coconut Aminos p46

Buy
Coconut Flour p88
Kimchi p80
Buckwheat Flakes p52

Printed in Great Britain
by Amazon

77830018R00058